Céad Míle
of
Welcome
benvenu,

Welcome to the newest edition of Ireland's Blue Book. Founded in 1974, we are a unique association comprising the country's finest Manor Houses, Castles, and Historic Hotels together with wonderful Restaurants, all over the island of Ireland. Each property has something different to offer in an enchanting and welcoming atmosphere.

For those of you seeking a scenic retreat or a gourmet getaway, there is somewhere perfect for you in our collection. For the more energetic among you, we have fishing, golf, cycling and equestrian pursuits. Included in our Blue Book are some very indulgent spas - if you want to be spoiled. You could combine business with pleasure and book your corporate occasions with us too. We have venues to cater for events of all tastes and sizes.

I would also like to welcome our new members, Belleek Castle in Co.Mayo; Hilton Park Manor House, Co.Monaghan; and The Tannery Restaurant & Townhouse, Co.Waterford. We are delighted to have them as part of the Blue Book Family.

With every good wish on behalf of all our members.

Sallyanne Clarke

Sallyanne Clarke
Chairperson of Ireland's Blue Book

IRISCHE LANDHÄUSER UND RESTAURANTS

Hinter dem Namen **Ireland's Blue Book** verbirgt sich ein exklusiver Zusammenschluss irischer Gastbetriebe, die in einzigartigen Land- und Herrenhäusern, Schlössern und Gourmetrestaurants untergebracht sind. Die Häuser der Blue Book- Mitglieder sind ideal für den anspruchsvollen Gast und bieten traditionelle irische Gastfreundschaft, erstklassige Unterbringung und Gourmetküche inmitten der anmutigen Schönheit der ländlichen Idylle Irlands.

CASAS DE CAMPO Y RESTAURANTES DE IRLANDA

Ireland's Blue Book es un exclusivo Grupo que reúne a las principales casas solariegas, hoteles históricos, castillos y restaurantes de Irlanda. Los establecimientos que se presentan en el Blue Book colmarán las expectativas de los visitantes más exigentes, atraídos por la serena belleza de la Irlanda rural ya sea en busca de hospitalidad tradicional, alojamiento o gastronomía de calidad.

RISTORANTI E DIMORE DI CAMPAGNA IRLANDESI

Ireland's Blue Book è un'associazione esclusiva che riunisce le dimore di campagna, gli hotel storici, i castelli e i ristoranti più belli del paese. Gli edifici descritti nel Blue Book non potranno fare a meno di attirare l'attenzione dei visitatori più esigenti in cerca di accoglienza tradizionale, ospitalità dagli standard elevati e cucina squisita nella serena bellezza della campagna irlandese.

RELAIS DE CAMPAGNE ET RESTAURANTS D'IRLANDE

Ireland's Blue Book est une association exceptionnelle qui rassemble les plus beaux manoirs, hôtels à caractère historique, châteaux et restaurants du pays. Les établissements présentés dans le Blue Book séduiront les visiteurs exigeants, à la recherche d'une hospitalité traditionnelle et raffinée, d'un hébergement de qualité et d'une cuisine savoureuse, au coeur de la beauté paisible d'une Irlande rurale.

魅力的なカントリーハウス・ホテルとレストラン

「アイルランド・ブルーブック」には、アイルランドで指折りのカントリー・ハウス、城、レストランが加盟しています。静かで美しいアイルランドの自然のなかで、伝統的に名高いアイルランド流「おもてなし」が体験できる、宿泊施設、レストランをお探しの方に、最適の場をご紹介しています。

HOW TO BOOK A BLUE BOOK HOUSE

Simply visit Ireland's Blue Book website and make your reservation/booking.

www.irelandsbluebook.com

Perhaps you are more comfortable dealing with a person rather than booking online. In this instance please contact the houses directly; they would love to hear from you. At the bottom of each page you will find the proprietor's name, address, telephone, email and website.

Reservations can also be made through your travel agent.

Reservation Agents in North America and Canada, please call

USA/Canada Toll Free 800 323 5463

Contact details
Ireland's Blue Book
63 Fitzwilliam Square
Dublin 2, Ireland

T +353 (0) 1 676 9914
USA/Canada Toll Free 800 323 5463
E mail@irelandsbluebook.com
www.irelandsbluebook.com

AHERNE'S TOWNHOUSE

Open fires and the warmest of welcomes await you in this family run hotel in the historic walled port of Youghal. Rooms are spacious and stylishly furnished. The famous Seafood Bar and Restaurant specialises in the freshest of Seafood (Lobster, Oysters, Crab, Prawns, Black Sole, Monkfish & Turbot) our bar is renowned for its friendliness; you can enjoy a chat with the locals along with your Guinness and Seafood. Gluten-free meals served for 30 years. Available for Intimate Weddings /Private Parties. Civil Marriage approved.

Local attractions: Walking, Swimming, Seaweed Baths, Horse Riding, Golfing, Sea Angling, Kayaking, Greyhound Racing, Jameson Heritage Centre, Fota Wildlife Park, Ardmore Cliff Walk, Blarney Castle, Waterford Crystal and Lismore Castle. Seaweed foraging, Ballymaloe cookery school, Cycling (greenway 20 mins)

Awards include:
Listed in the country's **top** 20 best Pubs in **Hot Press** Best of Ireland 2014.
Guardian Newspaper – 'One of the best breakfasts in Ireland'.
A Blue Book Voucher – complimentary upgrade where possible.

Bedrooms **12**   Guesthouse ★ ★ ★ ★

Aherne's, 163 North Main Street, Youghal, Co.Cork
T +353 (0)24 92424
F +353 (0)24 93633
info@ahernes.net
www.ahernes.com

Proprietor: The FitzGibbon Family
Open all year – except 4 days at Christmas.
Bed & Breakfast from €65 – €130 pps.
Single from €80 – €120.
Dinner served from 6pm to 9pm from €35.00.
Bar Food Service available Noon – 9pm daily.
Guide dogs welcome.

How to find:
Cork: 30 mins. (N25) Direction Rosslare.
Rosslare: 1.45hrs (N25).
Dublin: Take the N7 then the M7 onto the M9 to Waterford then take the N25 West to Youghal. 2.30hrs.

GPS coordinates
Lat: 51.957031634671
Long: -7.8518871130346

ARDTARA

In a secluded setting of 10 wooded acres, Ardtara is an elegant 19th century mansion in the heart of Northern Ireland. Within 45 minutes of the Giant's Causeway, the Antrim coast, Portstewart golf club, Derry and Belfast, it is the perfect base from which to explore.

Over the years Ardtara has been named the most romantic hotel of the year, listed amongst the best places to stay in Britain & Ireland and holds the current AA award for best guest accommodation in Northern Ireland.

With an emphasis on using seasonal local produce and fruit and vegetables from our gardens, the restaurant serves gastronomic feasts for dinner, sumptuous afternoon teas and Sunday lunch.

The house features a plethora of original features including working fireplaces, while each of the 9 king sized bedrooms are uniquely designed with full en suite facilities.

Recent Awards: Best guest accommodation in Northern Ireland 2016/17 **(AA)**. Best hotel restaurant in Ulster 2015 **(Irish Restaurants Association).**

Bedrooms **9**   **Listed Heritage Property**

**Ardtara Country House & Restaurant,
8 Gorteade Road, Upperlands,
Co. L'Derry BT46 5SA**
T +44 (0)28 796 44490
info@ardtara.com
www.ardtara.com

Proprietors: Roulston & Orr Families
Bed & Full Irish Breakfast from £49.50 – £70 pps.
Dinners & Sunday lunch available to all by reservation.
Dinner 5.30pm – 9.30pm à la carte.
Private Dining Room available by reservation.
Complimentary Wi-Fi on ground floor.

How to find:
Take M2/M22/A6 north toward Derry/Londonderry. 7 miles past the Castledawson roundabout, take A29 through Maghera. Continue on A29 towards Coleraine for three miles out of Maghera to the right turn on to B75. Proceed one mile into Upperlands. Ardtara sign is on the left towards the end of the village.

GPS coordinates
N 54.88297
W -6.636611

BALLYMALOE HOUSE

COUNTRY HOUSE & RESTAURANT

Family-run country house famous for outstanding hospitality and superb food. Produce is locally sourced and from their farm.

17th century house built on a Norman keep nestled in a 300 acre farm in rural East Cork. Located minutes from the coast and twenty miles from the historic city of Cork. Bedrooms range from elegant and airy to charming and cosy.

Facilities include extensive gardens, farm walks, tennis court, summer swimming pool, croquet lawn and Ballymaloe Grainstore. Ballymaloe Grainstore is an ideal venue for conferences, weddings and private events and hosts many cultural events year-round. The Ballymaloe Cookery School nearby is also run by the Allen family.

Awards include:
Condé Nast Traveler "Gold list 100 World's Best Hotels."
Food & Wine "Ireland's Top restaurants."
Georgina Campbell "Best breakfast in Ireland."
AA "Notable Wine List."

Bedrooms **29**   Guesthouse ★ ★ ★ ★

**Ballymaloe House, Shanagarry,
Co.Cork, P25 Y070**
T +353 (0)21 465 2531
res@ballymaloe.ie
www.ballymaloe.ie
#Ballymaloe - Facebook / Twitter / Instagram

How to find:
From Cork take N25 east. Then take R630 and R631. We are 2 miles beyond Cloyne on the Ballycotton road. From Waterford take N25 west to Castlemartyr. In Ladysbridge take care to follow signs to Cloyne, we are 2 miles from Ladysbridge on the Cloyne Road.

Proprietors: The Allen Family
Closed 24, 25, 26 December. 8 Jan. – 8 Feb.
Bed & Breakfast per person sharing.
Low season €105 – €137.50.
High season €125 – €155.
Service charge optional.
Dinner €75, from 7.00 – 9.30pm.
All major credit cards accepted.
Children welcome.

GPS coordinates
Latitude: 51.865083
Longitude: -8.075021

BARBERSTOWN CASTLE

Formerly the home of Eric Clapton and welcoming visitors for over 800 years, visitors to Barberstown will experience a very relaxing and welcoming Castle while enjoying great food, good wines, open log fires, luxury and exceptional personal service.

Use this unique Historic 13th Century Irish Castle as the ideal base from which to visit Dublin and Ireland's Ancient East. Enjoy 30 minutes carefree driving from or to Dublin Airport and 30 minutes from all the sites to visit in Dublin City Centre.

Essential Day Trips for your Vacation – Irish National Stud and Japanese Gardens. Drive to the Garden of Ireland in Wicklow visiting Russborough, Glendalough and Powerscourt. Newgrange (5,000 year old Megalithic site) and The Rock of Cashel are great day trips.

Awards include:
Best Historic Hotel of Europe CASTLE 2014 award.

Bedrooms **55 Ensuite**   Hotel ★ ★ ★ ★

Barberstown Castle, Straffan, Co.Kildare
T +353 (0)1 628 8157
F +353 (0)1 627 7027
info@barberstowncastle.ie
www.barberstowncastle.ie

Proprietor: Kenneth Healy
Open all year except three days Christmas, January and February
Bed & Breakfast Rates: €75 – €125 pps and €52.00 single room supplement.
Dinner: Table d'Hôte Menu available 6 – 8:30pm.
Lunch: Tea Rooms open daily 12 – 5pm.

GDS Codes:
HE DUBBCH, HE 29023, HE 30473, HE DUBBC

How to find:
Leave the airport and take the exit for the M50 South Bound. Leave the M50 at exit #7 (M4) and continue on the N4/M4 westward. Leave the M4 at Exit/Junction 7 (Straffan/Maynooth) and take the R407 to Straffan. (30 minutes - all Motorway).
Onward Journey: Because the Castle is minutes from the M1, M50, M4 and M7 motorways, it is the most perfect starting point, or final evening, on your Blue Book tour of Ireland. This Castle is easy to Find but hard to Leave!

Belleek Castle...an iconic Irish Country House, destination restaurant, hotel and spectacular wedding venue...

Built on an Abbey dating from mediaeval times, the 1820's neo-gothic Castle is informal, cosy, warm and friendly, rich in decor and antiquities, with open log fires to light your steps back through this cultural adventure.

Enjoy a contemporary dinner, with generous portions, in our unique eclectic dining room. We have developed a new food philosophy. Our spirit is to search for more "Depth of Flavour", exercising both classic and imaginative cooking techniques.

Delighted to design a wedding to suit in our dramatic Mediaeval Great Hall. Belleek Castle... Unique, intimate and magical.

Awards: **AA** 2 Rosettes, 2016: **Michelin Guide**, 2016: Best Castle Wedding Venue – **Mrs2B**, 2015–16: Top 100 Wedding Venue **One Fab Day**, 2014–16: **RAI** Best Hotel Restaurant, 2014–15: 16 Best Hotel Restaurant, 2014–15: Best Restaurant Manager, 2014: 'Just Ask' Restaurant of the Year **Georgina Campbell's.**

Bedrooms **10**

Specialist accommodation **Historic Castle**

Belleek Castle,
Ballina, Co.Mayo
T +353 (0) 96 22 400
info@belleekcastle.com
www.belleekcastle.com

Proprietors: The Doran Family
General Manager: Maya Nikolaeva
Closed January to mid February.
Rates €170 – €290.

How to find:
When coming in the Dublin/Foxford Road, continue driving towards Ballina. Go straight through the first two sets of traffic lights. Go straight on at the roundabout. After about 1km, go right onto the narrow road. After approx. 1 minute you will see a sign for Belleek Castle on your left-hand side.

GPS coordinates
N54° 07 59.1 W-009° 08 42.5
N54.13307 W-9.14513

In this Georgian country house standing at the head of Dunmanus Bay, everything revolves around the courtyard. Finely restored with cobbled paths, shrubs and flowers, it's 500 year old stone outbuildings contain four beautiful apartments as well as the restaurant with its magnificent dining room.

Blairscove Restaurant is best knows for it's buffet style starters and scrumptious desserts.

The elegant setting, the pretty courtyard and the landscaped gardens make it an ideal venue for weddings of up to 100 guests.

AA 2 rosettes 2016.
One Fab Day 100 best wedding venues 2016.
Tripadvisor certificate of Excellence 2016.
Michelin Guide 2016.
AA*****Gold Star Awards 2016 Restaurant with rooms.

Bedrooms **4 courtyard suites, self catering also available**

Blairscove House, Durrus near Bantry, Co.Cork
T +353 (0)27 61127
mail@blairscove.ie
www.blairscove.ie

Proprietors: The De Mey Family
Restaurant: Open from March 16th to October 29th 2017.
Tuesday to Saturday 6:30pm – 9:30pm.
3 course table d'hôte menu €60.
Accommodation: Open from March 16th to October 29th, 2017.
Bed & Breakfast €75 – €130 midweek.
Friday & Saturday €110 – €130.
Single supplement €30.
Major credit cards accepted.

How to find: Coming from Durrus follow the R591 to Crook haven. After 1.5 miles you'll see the blue gate on the right hand side.
Cork airport: 1 hr 15 mins.

GPS coordinates
51 degrees 36' 33" N
9 degrees 32' 18" W

BROWNS RESTAURANT
& CHAMPAGNE LOUNGE

Since rebirth in 2009, "Browns Restaurant" has gained a reputation for excellent food, genuine hospitality and great service. The critics have not only established this multi-award winning restaurant as the best in the North West but have placed it among the best in Ireland.

Located in the heart of the iconic city of Derry and overlooking the River Foyle, Browns with its Art Deco interior is the sister restaurant to Ardtara Country House.

Chef Patron Ian Orr, driven by his passion for great local produce and seasonality is tipped as one of Ireland's top talents and the awards and critical acclaim have flowed over the years:

Restaurants Association of Ireland	Best Restaurant in Northern Ireland 2016 Best Wine Experience in Northern Ireland 2016.
Michelin Guide	Recommended.
Georgina Campbell	Ireland's Chef of the Year 2013.

Covers **70**

Browns Restaurant & Champagne Lounge, 1 Bonds Hill Derry/Londonderry, BT47 6DW
T +44 (0)28 7134 5180
eat@brownsrestaurant.com
www.brownsrestaurant.com

Proprietors: Ian Orr & Marcus Roulston
Opening Hours:

Lunch: Tuesday-Friday	12:00pm – 3:00pm.
Sunday lunch:	12:00pm – 3:30pm.
Dinner: Tuesday – Thursday	5:30pm – 9:00pm.
Dinner: Friday-Saturday	5:00pm – 10:00pm.

Lunch Menu 3 courses:	£15.
Dinner set menu 3 courses:	£21.95.
Dinner a la carte 3 courses:	from £30.

How to find: Browns Restaurant is located on the east side of Lough Foyle just off the A2 at the junction of A2 and Bonds Hill.

GPS coordinates
54.993418
-7.312089

BUSHMILLS INN HOTEL

The Bushmills Inn is situated in an enviable location a stone's throw from The Giant's Causeway, Royal Portrush, Dunluce Castle and Game of Thrones filming locations. Roaring peat fires, nooks and crannies and a secret library set the tone.

In the bar, still lit by gas light, try a glass of malt from the hotel's private cask and sample the finest North Antrim produce in the AA Rosette restaurant.

Whether you wish to linger by the fire, enjoy afternoon tea on the garden courtyard, partake in water sports, hike in unspoilt countryside or play golf on some of Ireland's finest courses, the Bushmills Inn is the ideal location.

Awards include:
TripAdvisor Travellers' Choice Awards 2016.
Northern Ireland Tourism Awards Customer Service Excellence 2016.
Best Loved Hotels Best Hotel in Ireland 2015.
Northern Ireland Tourism Awards Hotel of the Year 2015.
AA Hotel of the Year for Northern Ireland 2014 – 2015.

Bedrooms **41**   Specialist accommodation **Historic Building**   Hotel ★ ★ ★ ★

Bushmills Inn Hotel, 9 Dunluce Road, Bushmills, Co.Antrim, BT57 8QG
T + 44(0)28 207 33000
mail@bushmillsinn.com
www.bushmillsinn.com

Proprietor: Alan Dunlop
Hotel Manager: Alan Walls
Open all year Monday to Sunday.
Restaurant open all day: 12 noon to 9.30,
dinner 6pm to 9.30pm Stg£30.
B&B: Low Season: Oct – Mar from £60 pps.
High Season: April – Sept from £100 pps.
All bedrooms non-smoking.
Credit Cards: Amex, Mastercard, Visa.

How to find:
From Belfast follow the M2 north to Ballymena then A26 to Ballymoney. At the roundabout take the third exit onto B62 heading to Portrush/ Bushmills, turn right onto Priestland Road (B17) then right onto Dunluce Road (A2). The Bushmills Inn will be on the left.

GPS coordinates
N 55 12' 25.64"
W 6 31' 26.63"

Campagne restaurant in Kilkenny city opened in 2008. The emphasis has been to serve food based on high-quality seasonal produce with French influences in a relaxed and comfortable dining area.

Located under the old railway arches on Gas House Lane, Campagne boasts a stylish interior featuring oak flooring, curved banquette leather seating and modern paintings depicting rural life by Kilkenny artist Catherine Barron.

Campagne has been awarded many prestigious awards on a national and international level, most notably one Michelin star status in September 2013.

At Campagne we have a passionately held philosophy that supports and showcases the very best of quality food and wine producers.

Campagne Restaurant
5 The Arches, Gas House Lane, Kilkenny
T +353 (0)56 777 2858
info@campagne.ie www.campagne.ie

Proprietors: Garrett Byrne & Brid Hannon
Opening hours:
Closed Sunday nights and all day Monday.
Lunch: Friday and Saturday 12.30pm – 2.30pm.
Sunday Lunch: 12.30pm – 3.00pm.
Early Bird: Tuesday – Thursday 6pm – 7pm
(5.30pm – 6pm on Fridays and Saturdays).
Dinner: Tuesday – Saturday 6pm – 10pm,
Open Sunday nights on Bank Holidays, closed on
Tuesday nights following Bank Holiday.
Annual Holidays: Last two weeks in January and
first week in July.

How to find:
Campagne is located just under the cities old
railway arches, in an area called John's green,
the restaurant is in close proximity to Mc Donagh
Junction shopping centre.

GPS coordinates
52"8304;39'21" N
7"8304;14'47" W

CARRIG COUNTRY HOUSE

Hidden away on the shores of Caragh Lake, Ring of Kerry, enchanting 'Carrig' offers an 'escape from it all' and the most beautiful scenery in Ireland.

Enjoy golf, fishing, horse riding or hiking. Tour the Ring of Kerry, Dingle Peninsula, Killarney National Park or World Heritage Site Skellig Michael.

Snuggle up in a comfy king size bed and awake to the sound of the lake lapping on the shore. Stroll the wonderful gardens (950 species) or indulge in a good book or game of chess in the spacious Drawing Rooms.

Savour fine wines and mouth-watering Irish Country House cooking in our award winning **Lakeside Restaurant**. Frank, Mary and Team extend a warm welcome and unique Irish Country House experience.

Gold Medal Awards "Ireland's Country House 2015/16."
Irish Restaurant Awards Best Chef in Kerry 2015.
Georgina Campbell's Ireland Guide "Country House of the Year 2013."
Good Hotel Guide Editors Choice.
FODOR's International Guide – "Fodor's Choice."

Bedrooms **17**   Suites **2**   Country House ★ ★ ★ ★

Carrig Country House & Restaurant,
Caragh Lake, Killorglin, Co.Kerry V93 WK83
T +353 (0)66 976 9100
info@carrighouse.com www.carrighouse.com

Hosts / Proprietors: Frank & Mary Slattery
Closed November – February inclusive.
Bed & breakfast per person sharing:
€75 – €155 pps Low Season.
€95 – €195 pps High Season.
Single supplement €60.
2 & 3 Day Value Package price on
www.carrighouse.com
Dinner: A La Carte or Dinner Menu available from
6.30-9pm.
Visa, Mastercard, Maestro Accepted.
Children over the age of 8 years are welcome.

How to find:
From Killorglin (10 minutes) – N70 from Killorglin towards Glenbeigh for 4km. After PROMED offices, take 2nd left for Caragh Lake (signposted). At Caragh Lake School and Shop see signpost for Carrig, take sharp right, located 1km further on the left.
From Glenbeigh (10 minutes) – Take the N70 in the direction of Killorglin for 4km, go over one-way stone bridge turning right, continue for approx. 1km and turn right onto the Caragh Lake road (Carrig signpost, before the Red Fox Inn) and drive for 2km. Carrig Country House is on the right.

GPS coordinates
N 52 4' 26.23"
W 9 51' 0.58"

CASHEL HOUSE HOTEL COUNTRY HOUSE & RESTAURANT

A perfect start of your adventure on the Wild Atlantic Way – Cashel House formerly one of Connemara's most gracious homes, set in 50 acres of magnificent gardens on the beautiful coastline of Cashel Bay with Cashel Hill rising behind.

Owned by the McEvilly Family for 50 years, where a warm welcome awaits you. Relax in our Drawing Room with open log fires, antiques and fine arts. Retire to comfortable bedrooms all individually decorated or dine in our restaurant overlooking the garden which serves the finest local seafood and meat dishes with vegetables from our garden and region.

Enjoy walking, beaches, sea and lake fishing, riding, hiking, golf, Connemara ponies in our stud farm, visit to Kylemore Gardens, travel to Aran and Inish Boffin islands or take a boat trip off Killary Fjord.

Awards: **AA** Inspector Choice Award, **AA** 2 Rosettes & included in 1000 places to see before you die.

Bedrooms **16**   Suites **13**   Hotel ★ ★ ★ ★

Cashel House Hotel, Cashel, Connemara, Co.Galway, H91 XE10
T +353 (0)95 31001
sales@cashelhouse.ie
www.cashelhouse.ie

Proprietors: The McEvilly Family
Closed January and reopen on 11 February.
Bed & Breakfast per person sharing
€75 – €165 pps Low Season.
€95 – €230 pps High Season.
Children welcome.
Special Breaks on request.
Dinner: 3 course €32.00, 5 course €55.00,
A la Carte also available.
All major credit cards accepted.

Pet friendly.
Exclusive wedding parties 120 max.
Gratuity at your discretion.

How to find:
South off N59 (Galway Clifden Road).
1.6 kilometres (1 mile) west of Recess, turn left.

GPS coordinates
53.419547
-9.807950

CASTLE DURROW

Built by Viscount Ashbrook in 1716, in the picturesque village of Durrow, Co.Laois conveniently located about 1 hour from Dublin and 1.5 hours from Cork. Lovingly restored and family home to Peter and Shelly Stokes, Castle Durrow is now one of Ireland's magnificent luxury four star hotels and proudly one of Ireland's most popular wedding venues.

Explore the estate, the surrounding woodlands and river pathways or stroll through our amazing gardens where lots of our organic kitchen produce is grown. Visit the Cafes, Bars, Restaurants and Shops of Durrow, the nearby Heritage Town of Abbeyleix and surrounding historic sites at Kilkenny Castle and Rock of Cashel both 30 mins.

TripAdvisor – Top 10 Castle Hotels of the World, Hall of Fame winner 2015.
Irish Restaurant Association Awards Winner – 2010 up to and including 2016.
One Fab Day – Top 100 wedding Venues in Ireland.

Bedrooms **46 and quirky Gate Lodge**

Castle Durrow, Durrow, Co.Laois
T +353 (0)57 873 6555
F +353 (0)57 873 6559
info@castledurrow.com
www.castledurrow.com
www.facebook.com/CastleDurrow

Proprietors: The Stokes Family
Open all year but closed for Christmas
24–26 December inc.
Restaurant Open Wednesday – Sunday.
Dinner, Bed & Breakfast from €220 per couple.
Four Course Dinner from €39.50 per person.
Sunday Lunch from €29.50 per person.
Afternoon tea from €19.50 per person.
Private Dining Rooms available for special
occasions.

How to find:
From Dublin: On M7 take exit 17 then N77
through Abbeyleix to Durrow.
From Cork: On M8 take exit 4 then R639
through Johnstown, Cullohill to Durrow.

GPS Coordinates:
Lat: 52.846301
Long: -7.401223

Steeped in history, full of character and charm, Castle Leslie Estate is the ultimate Irish rural escape. Nestled on 1,000 acres of undulating Irish countryside, dotted with ancient woodland and glittering lakes, Castle Leslie Estate, is one of the last great Irish castle estates still in the hands of its founding family.

The Castle, at the heart of the Estate, offers authentic original interiors and old-style hospitality.

The Lodge, our country house style boutique hotel has 29 rooms – each of which remain true to the building's original structure. Explore the Estate on horseback, enjoy some of Ireland's finest coarse fishing, luxuriate in a relaxing massage or just a stroll through the woods – just some of the choices that await you in this hidden corner of Ireland.

Hotel and Catering Review Gold Medal Award:
Best Hotel Breakfast – The Castle at Castle Leslie.
AA Courtesy and Care Award 2015 – 2016:
The Lodge at Castle Leslie Estate.

Bedrooms **49**   Specialist accommodation **Historic Castle**

Castle Leslie Estate, Glaslough, Co.Monaghan
T +353 (0)47 88100
info@castleleslie.com
www.castleleslie.com

Proprietor: Sammy Leslie
General Manager: Brian Baldwin
Bed and Breakfast:
From €95pps at The Lodge
From €115pps at The Castle.

Single occupancy (Bed and Breakfast)
From €170 at The Lodge
From €210 at The Castle.

How to find:
From Dublin take M1 north. Exit at Junction 14 for Ardee. Follow N2 Monaghan/Derry. Continue on the N2 to Monaghan bypass – do not enter town. 1st roundabout follow N2 for Derry. Continue to 3rd roundabout. Take 3rd exit signposted Armagh (N12). Follow N12 for 2 miles. Turn left at signpost for Glaslough (R185). Follow road to Glaslough. 80 minutes from Dublin, 60 minutes from Belfast.

GPS coordinates
Lat: 54.31821
Long: -6.89582

Garmin Loc8 code
G6E-22-5TK

CHAPTER ONE RESTAURANT

Chapter One Restaurant is located in Dublin city centre on the north side of Parnell Square. As a former home of John Jameson, it retains authentic granite walls and sash windows and has been carefully and stylishly renovated to create a wonderfully sumptuous and comfortable restaurant.

It is one of Dublin's leading restaurants having won numerous awards for both food and service. The front of house team are warm and friendly while retaining a high level of efficiency and professionalism.

It is Dublin's premier pre-theatre dining venue. Chapter One proprietor, Ross Lewis has continued to strive for excellence and this effort is manifest throughout the restaurant. A rare treat awaits you.

Chapter One Restaurant
18/19 Parnell Square, Dublin
T +353 (0)1 873 2266
F +353 (0)1 873 2330
info@chapteronerestaurant.com
www.chapteronerestaurant.com

How to find:
Centre of Dublin – Parnell Square
is at the top of O'Connell Street.

Proprietor: Ross Lewis
Opening hours:
Lunch: Tuesday – Friday 12.30 – 2.00.
Dinner: Tuesday – Saturday 5.30 – 10.00.
Annual Holidays: Christmas – two weeks;
August – two weeks.
Private Dining: The Jameson Room: 14 people.
The Vault Room: 16 people.

CLARE ISLAND LIGHTHOUSE

The 200 year old Lighthouse, situated on Clare Island in Clew Bay Co. Mayo, has been completely restored and opened for guests in 2013. Its location high on the cliffs, 120 meters above the sea, enables a spectacular vista over the Atlantic Ocean and surrounding areas.

Our interiors, in keeping with the ethos of the Lighthouse, are understated but exceedingly comfortable.

This eclectic heritage lighthouse offers "sumptuous" elegant food based on local produce: fish and lamb are regularly showcased on the dinner menu complimented by a good selection of International wines.
There's lots to do... Walking, swimming, hiking, cycling, bird watching, reading or simply relaxing beside a turf fire.

Clare Island Lighthouse is one of the GREAT LIGHTHOUSES of Ireland on the Wild Atlantic Way.

Trip Advisor – Certificate of excellence 2016.
Boutique Hotel awards nominee 2016.

Accommodation **6 bedrooms/Suites**   Specialist accommodation **Lighthouse**

Clare Island Lighthouse
T +353 (0)87 668 9758
info@clareislandlighthouse.com
bookinglighthouse@gmail.com
www.clareislandlighthouse.com

Proprietor: The Fischer Family
General Manager: Ms Roie Mc Cann
March 31st – October 1st, 2017.
Children over 16.
Minimum 2 night stay.
€400 – €500 pps for 2 nights.
Includes BB and 6 course Dinner.
Single supplement €100.
Visa and MasterCard accepted.

How to find:
Directions from Westport to Clare Island –
Take the R335 to Louisburgh (20km).
Approximately 1.5km after Louisburgh town take a right turn for Roonagh Pier (approx 7km).
The ferry sails from Roonagh Pier to Clare Island. (20 minutes approx.).

GPS coordinates
53.82822 N
-9.98340 E

COOPERSHILL HOUSE

2 hours from Dublin in the dramatic North West, a genuine, romantic, Grand Irish Country House with comfort, character and **sublime cooking.**

A stunning mile long avenue crossing the River Unshin and winding through ancient woods and deer pastures on the 500 acre Private Estate brings you to this fabulous Georgian mansion. Coopershill has been the family home to 8 generations of O'Haras and personal attention from the owners is guaranteed.

The perfect base for exploring WB Yeats country, Lissadell House, links golf, hiking around our lakes, mountains & neolithic tombs and surfing & horse riding on empty beaches.

Recent Accolades:
Sunday Telegraph 2016 Best 3 Irish Country House Hotels.
John & Sally McKenna's 2016 100 Best Places to Stay.
Restaurant Association 2016 Best Hotel Restaurant Sligo.

Recommended by Alistair Sawday, Georgina Campbell, Andrew Harper, Good Hotel Guide, Karen Brown, Fodor's and all good guide books.

Bedrooms **8**   Specialist accommodation **Historic House**

Coopershill House, Riverstown, Co.Sligo, F52 EC52
T +353 (0)71 916 5108
ohara@coopershill.com
www.coopershill.com

Proprietor: The O'Hara Family
Open April to end of October.
Open all year for house parties.
Bed & Breakfast
from €101 – €112 pps low season
from €112 – €125 pps high season.
Single supplement €50.
4 course dinner at 8.00pm €56 p/p.

How to find:
On N4 route to Dublin 19km south-east of Sligo. At crossroads follow signs to Riverstown and Coopershill.

GPS coordinates
N 54.1381
W 8.4154

CURRAREVAGH HOUSE

Old fashioned (in the best sense of the word), Currarevagh is situated on the shores of Lough Corrib in 150 acres of private woodland estate, now a European Special Area of Conservation. It is run as a private country house rather than an hotel, and the tranquil informality lends itself to those seeking to escape today's hectic world.

Built by the present owner's ancestors in 1842, the exceptional food, cooked by Lucy with flair, originality and passion, and magical grounds take centre stage. Having Connemara and the Aran Islands within easy touring reach, our own boats for guest's use, many walks and abundant wildlife – it all makes a unique, original and wonderful experience not to be missed.

Recent accolades:

Tripadvisor Traveller's Choice 2016 Top 25 Small Hotels in Ireland.

Recommended by Alistair Sawday, Georgina Campbell, Good Hotel Guide, Michelin Guide, Karen Brown and others.
Sunday Telegraph Review – 9/10 (Fiona Duncan).

Bedrooms **12**   Guesthouse ★ ★ ★ ★

Currarevagh House, Oughterard, Connemara, Co.Galway
T +353 (0)91 552312
  +353 (0)91 552313
F +353 (0)91 552731
rooms@currarevagh.com
www.currarevagh.com

Proprietors: The Hodgson Family
Open 16 March to 31 October.
Bed and Breakfast from €70.00 – €90.00 pps.
Single Rooms available.
Dinner €50.00.

How to find:
Take the N59 (Galway/ Clifden) road to Oughterard. Turn right in village square and follow the Glann road for 6kms.

Extra information:
Reduced Half Board Rates for visits of 2 or more days. Weekly half board rate from €820 pp per week.
Out of season house parties are welcome (excluding Christmas and New Year).

GPS coordinates
N 53 27.657
W 9 21.518

DUNBRODY HOUSE

Indulgence is the order of the day at Dunbrody with world-renowned gourmet restaurant, chic champagne seafood bar and breakfast til Noon daily. Couple this foodie focus with our aim to please and pamper and you get a feel for what Dunbrody House is loved for. Set in 300 acres of parkland on the idyllic Hook Peninsula on Ireland's south coast 1830s Dunbrody really is the perfect year-round choice for a romantic getaway to the country.

For the culinary inquisitives there's the temptation of our cookery school with a range of 1, 2 & 5 day courses and for those seeking some me-time there's the luxury boutique Spa.

Tasting the craft beers from our micro-brewery and sampling of the "craic" in our traditional Irish pub "The Local" are also musts.

"Ease, Elegance, Excellence" Seamus Heaney, Poet Laureate.

Bedrooms **22** including Suites and Guest Lodge   Hotel ★ ★ ★ ★

Dunbrody Country House Hotel, Arthurstown,Y34 R597 Co. Wexford
T +353 (0)51 389600
F +353 (0)51 389601
info@dunbrodyhouse.com
www.dunbrodyhouse.com

Proprietors: Catherine & Kevin Dundon
B&B from €75 – €155 pps low season,
€95 – €195 pps high season.
Single Supplement €25 per night on
standard double rooms.
Seasonal 5 course Dinner Menu €65 and
€80 8 course Tasting Menu.

How to find:
M11/N11 from south Dublin and then the R733 to Arthurstown.
M9 from north Dublin to New Ross and then the R733 to Arthurstown.
N25 from Cork/Waterford and the Passage East car ferry to Ballyhack.

ENNISCOE HOUSE

Hidden among the woods at the foot of Nephin is Enniscoe, 'the last Great House of North Mayo' overlooking the waters of Lough Conn. The estate has been in the family since the 1650's and the classical Georgian house dates from the 1790's.

The current generation, Susan Kellett and her son Dj, are happy to share their house and grounds with guests. There are elegant reception rooms and fine bedrooms with stunning views over lake and park. Outside are pastures, shrubberies, miles of woodland and lakeside walks, a carefully restored Victorian pleasure garden and an organic vegetable garden. Good food, freshly prepared, uses fruit and vegetables from the garden as well as other local produce.

Bedrooms **6**   Specialist accommodation **Historic House**

Enniscoe House, Castlehill, Ballina, Co.Mayo
T +353 (0)96 31112
mail@enniscoe.com
www.enniscoe.com

Proprietor: Susan Kellett and Dj Kellett
Open 1 April to 31 October.
Bed & Breakfast from €85 – €125 pps.
Dinner €50 at 7.30 / 8.00pm.
Single supplement €30.
Dogs welcome.

How to find:
Enniscoe is 3.2km south of the village of Crossmolina on the R315 to Pontoon and Castlebar. It is 20km from Ballina.

Ireland West Airport Knock 50 km.

GPS coordinates
N Lat. 54075060
W. 9312633

GHAN HOUSE

Built in 1727, Ghan House is a listed Georgian House and Restaurant set within 3 acres of walled mature gardens.

It is just a tree length from medieval Carlingford, with its' narrow streets, town gate, castles, priory & ancient walls. Ghan House is one hour from Dublin and Belfast.

The 2 AA Rosette awarded restaurant utilises the herb & vegetable gardens and celebrates its' position on Carlingford Lough with the local seafood and Cooley mountain lamb and beef.

Whether you stay in the old house or one of the garden bedrooms, views of Carlingford Lough, the Mourne mountains or Slieve Foy come as standard.

Awards:
2 **AA** Rosettes since 2011.
4* **AA** accommodation.
John & Sally McKenna's "Best 100 Places to stay in Ireland" every year since 1999.
'Alastair Sawday' recommended every year since 1999.

Bedrooms **12**   Specialist accommodation **Historic House**

Ghan House, Carlingford, Co.Louth
T +353 (0)42 937 3682
info@ghanhouse.com
www.ghanhouse.com

Proprietor: Paul & Joyce Carroll
Open all year.
(Closed 24 – 26th, 31st December & 1st & 2nd January).
B&B from €80 pps – €125 pps.
4 course dinner €49.50, most nights 6pm – 9.30pm.
6 course midweek tasting menu €39.50 6pm to 7.45pm.
Special midweek & weekend dinner & B&B breaks.
All major credit cards accepted.

No service charge. Gratuities at discretion of guests.

How to find:
Take junction 18 on main Dublin to Belfast M1 to Carlingford. On the left, 10 metres after 50kph sign on entrance to Carlingford is a stone entrance & gravel drive to Ghan House.

GPS coordinates
N54°02.373' W006°11.044' / 54.04028, - 6.18417

GREGANS CASTLE

With breathtaking views across Galway Bay and idyllically situated overlooking the unique Burren landscape, this is the ultimate luxury and gourmet hideaway.

Simon and Frederieke together with their staff manage this oasis of comfort and offer genuine Irish hospitality, award winning innovative cooking and elegant bedrooms free from the intrusion of televisions. Antiques, an eclectic art collection, open fires, candles, jugs of flowers and Shelley the cat add to the indulgently relaxing atmosphere.

Located on the Wild Atlantic Way and the Burren Food Trail. The ideal location from which to enjoy the Burren, Cliffs of Moher, Walking, Cycling, the Aran Islands, Horse Riding, Surfing, Sea Angling, Golf. Members of The Burren Ecotourism Network.

Awards include: **Georgina Campbell's** Hotel of the Year 2016, **RAI** Best Hotel Restaurant 2016, **Gold Medal Awards** Ireland's Chef of the Year 2015, Supreme Winner & Best Country House 2014; **Food & Wine Magazine** Best Restaurant & Best Chef Munster 2014; **AA** 3 Rosettes for Culinary Excellence.

Bedrooms **15**   Suites **6**   Hotel ★ ★ ★ ★

Gregans Castle Hotel, The Burren, Ballyvaughan, Co. Clare, H91 CF60
T +353 (0)65 7077005
stay@gregans.ie
www.gregans.ie

Proprietors: Simon Haden and Frederieke McMurray
General Manager: Ken Bergin
Bed & Breakfast from €245.00 per room per night for two persons sharing.
Dinner from €45.00 to €72.00.

Open from February 17th to November 4th inclusive.

How to find:
On N67, 5km south of Ballyvaughan village. Only 1 hour from Shannon Airport and 2½ hours from Dublin.

GPS coordinates
53 04 36 79 N
9 11 11 19 W

HAYFIELD MANOR

Nestled within secluded gardens, Cork's premier 5 star hotel, Hayfield Manor provides the charm of a country house within the vibrant city of Cork. Splendid rooms and suites are classically styled and individually decorated. Guests with a penchant for exquisite food should sample the local fare showcased in the gourmet restaurant, Orchids, and in the contemporary dining space, Perrotts Garden Bistro. A delightful white-glove Afternoon Tea is also served daily.

The Beautique Spa features Elemis Spa Therapy, with pool, Jacuzzi, sauna, steam room and resident's gym. The concierge will assist you to discover the unique attractions of Cork city and county.

Awards include: **Georgina Campbell's** Ireland Hotel of the Year, **Fodor's** Choice Award, **AA** Irish Hotel of the Year, **RAC** Gold Ribbon Award for Excellence. **Tripadvisor** Traveller's Choice Award, **Conde Nast** Reader's Choice Award.

Bedrooms **88**   Suites **4**   Hotel ★ ★ ★ ★ ★

Hayfield Manor, Perrott Avenue, College Road, T12 HT97, Cork City
T +353 (0)21 484 5900
F +353 (0)21 431 6839
enquiries@hayfieldmanor.ie
www.hayfieldmanor.ie

Proprietors: Joe and Margaret Scally
Manager: Ettienne Van Vrede
Open all year round.
Manor Rooms: €99 pps to €190 pps.
Superior and Deluxe Rooms also available.
Suites: €245 pps to €650 pps.
Perrotts Garden Bistro: A la Carte.
Orchids: 5 course Gourmet Menu – €69 per person.
Afternoon Tea: 1pm – 4.30pm.
Private dining available.

Service charge of 10% on 8 people or more.
All major credit cards accepted.
Wheelchair accessible rooms available.

How to find:
6 miles from Cork International Airport (ORK), 80 miles from Shannon International Airport (SNN). Hayfield Manor is located off College Road, opposite UCC.
GDS codes: Amadeus- LX ORKHMR, Apollo/Galileo- LX 78441, Sabre- LX 31327, Worldspan- LX ORKHM

GPS coordinates
N 51.89102
W -8.48953

HILTON PARK

Hilton Park is a "majestic one off". Now lived in by the 9th & 10th generations, the Madden family have been welcoming guests to their home for over 30 years. Highly skilled cuisine, home-grown produce and an intimate but extremely relaxing atmosphere, gives the guest a uniquely authentic experience. Staying at Hilton truly is an experience, with fine portraits and paintings, antique furniture and an atmosphere that cannot be reproduced.

The house is set in stunning grounds, with majestic views from all windows. With over 600 acres of parkland, lakes, superb woodlands, croquet lawn and a historic herb and walled gardens; complimentary golf is also available.

Ideal for private parties and people looking for an alternative to the conventional hotel experience. Just 90 minutes from Dublin and Belfast airports.

Awards include:
Good Hotel Guide – Editor's Choice Historic Hotel 2016.
Good Hotel Guide – Cesar Award.
Featured in **Conde Nast Traveller** – Ireland's Best Country House Hotels.

Bedrooms **6**

Hilton Park
Clones, Co.Monaghan, Ireland
T +353 (0)47 56007
mail@hiltonpark.ie
www.hiltonpark.ie

Proprietor: Fred and Joanna Madden
Open March 25th 2016 – October 31st 2016
Open for groups throughout the year (8 or more guests).
Principal Bedrooms, with Four Poster or Tester Beds: €240 – €270 per room per night, including full Irish breakfast.
Double and Twin Bedrooms: €180 – €240 per room per night, including full Irish breakfast
Complimentary golf and fishing.
Dinner €60 for a 4 course set menu, book previous day.

How to find:
From Dublin take N3 to Cavan. At roundabout on approaching Cavan take by-pass, signed Ballyshannon and Monaghan. Leave by-pass to the right at second junction and follow signs to BALLYHAISE. Go through Ballyhaise and then Scotshouse, heading for Clones and in about 2 miles we are the next entry on the left after the Clones Golf Club. From Belfast, The North and Donegal head for Clones.

GPS coordinates
54°08'35.9"N, 7°14'10.4"W
54.143308, -7.236218

HUNTER'S HOTEL

Ireland's oldest coaching inn, in the 5th generation of the same family. Its picturesque gardens along the banks of the river Vartry provide a delightful setting for a delicious lunch, afternoon tea or a drink.

An ideal base from which to visit Mount Usher Gardens, Powerscourt, Russborough, Killruddery and Glendalough in County Wicklow, 'The Garden of Ireland'.

There are fifteen 18-hole golf courses nearby, most notably Druid's Glen and the European. Horse riding and hill walking can be arranged. Conference facilities available. Hunter's is approx. 60 minutes drive from Dublin, 30 minutes from Dun Laoghaire and 90 minutes from Rosslare.

Bedrooms **16**   Specialist accommodation **Hotel & Restaurant**

Hunter's Hotel, Newrath Bridge, Rathnew, Co.Wicklow
T +353 (0)404 40106
facebook.com/pages/HuntersIreland
reception@hunters.ie
www.hunters.ie

Proprietor: Gelletlie Family
Closed 24, 25, 26 & 31 December.
Bed & Breakfast from €65 – €95 per person.
Dinner from €29.50 served 7.30pm to 8.45pm.
Lunch from €19.75 served 1.00pm to 2.30pm.
Sunday Lunch from €35.00 served from 12.45pm.
Afternoon Tea from €15.00 served from 4.00pm.
Private dining available.
No Service Charge.

How to find:
From Dublin: Take exit 15 for Ashford off the N11.
Turn left at the bridge in Ashford. Then 2km.
From Wexford/Rosslare: Take exit 16 for
Ashford off the N11. Pass Mount Usher Gardens.
Turn right at the bridge in Ashford. Then 2km.

GPS coordinates
N 53.006374
W -6.084328

ICE HOUSE

The Ice House is a wonderful fusion of old and new. Rooms and suites with panoramic views to the river Moy marry the beauty of the original 18th century building with contemporary styling. Be pampered with VOYA treatments in Chill Spa. Relax in the thermal suite, outdoor hot tubs and barrel sauna. Enjoy fabulous food by Chef Anthony Holland - the best of fresh and local.

On the Wild Atlantic Way, close to Ireland West Airport, here's the perfect base for exploring the stunning coastline of the North West.

Irish Tatler Best Boutique Spa/ Best Therapist
Irish Hair & Beauty Awards Best Spa 2016
Golfers Guide to Ireland Best Boutique Hotel

'Excellent food, dreamlike treatments, and a view that you'll throw a tantrum about having to leave behind,' Beaut.ie.

'Swish, small and delightfully situated. An excellent boutique hotel that offers an experience that is second to none,' Neil Hegarty, The Telegraph.

Bedrooms / Suites **32**   Hotel ★ ★ ★ ★

The Ice House, The Quay, Ballina, Co.Mayo
T +353 (0)96 23500
chill@theicehouse.ie
www.theicehouse.ie

Proprietor: Pearse Farrell
Open all year round.
Closed 23 – 26 December.
Deluxe Rooms from €69 pps B&B,
Suites from €89 pps B&B.
Single Occupancy supplement €50.
Dinner served 6pm to 9pm, €45.
Bar Menu served 1pm to 9pm.
Sunday Lunch 1pm to 3pm, €25.
Children welcome.

How to find:
From Dublin – Follow N4/M4 route direction Sligo. At Longford follow N5 route direction Westport. Turn right onto N26 outside Swinford direction Foxford and Ballina. On arrival in Ballina, follow N59 direction Sligo through the town and across the river. Turn left at traffic lights onto Quay Road. The Ice House is located ca. 1km on The Quay.

Killarney town's most charming boutique hotel. For three generations, our family has held the mantle of caring for guests at the 4 star Killarney Royal, where visitors have been welcomed for over 100 years. Committed to delivering gracious hospitality and creating outstanding memories, we and our wonderful team deliver friendly personal service and true Irish hospitality.

We provide luxurious accommodation, exceptional and innovative cuisine and, with our town centre location, the ideal abode from which to explore the bustling town of Killarney. Our door is always open and we look forward to welcoming you very soon.

Awards include:

IGTOA Boutique Golf Hotel of the Year Award.
TripAdvisor Travellers Choice.
Lucinda O'Sullivan's Little Black Book of 'Great Places To Stay'.

Bedrooms **32**   Suites **5**   Hotel ★ ★ ★ ★

**Killarney Royal, College Street,
Killarney Town, V93 XC90, Co. Kerry**
T +353 (0)64 6631853
F +353 (0)64 6634001
reception@killarneyroyal.ie
www.killarneyroyal.ie

**Proprietors: Joe and Margaret Scally
Manager: Claire Scally**
Closed 24, 25, 26 December.
Royal Rooms: €49.50 pps to €160.00 pps.
Deluxe and Junior Suites also available.
Suites: €74.50 pps to €180.00 pps.
The Royal Bar & Bistro: A la Carte.
The Candle Room Restaurant: €29.95 per person.
Afternoon Tea for Two: €27.00 (January –
November) & €32 for Christmas Afternoon Tea.
Private dining available.

Service charge of 10% on 8 people or more.
All major cards accepted.

How to find:
140 meters from Killarney train station
11mi /17km From Kerry International Airport
54mi /87km From Cork International Airport
84mi /135kms From Shannon International Airport
GDS Codes: Amadeus: LM KIR170,
Galileo/Apollo: LM 38135,
Sabre: LM 060601,
WorldSpan: LM 08170

GPS coordinates
N 52.059787
W -9.506131

KING SITRIC
FISH RESTAURANT & ACCOMMODATION

Located in the picturesque fishing village of Howth, established 1971, the MacManus family have built an international reputation for warm hospitality along with fresh local seafood. Panoramic sea views, the lapping of the water, the sounds of the sea birds... only 20 minutes from Dublin Airport and 25 minutes by DART into Dublin City.

Lobster, Crab and Shrimp are caught by our local fishermen in Balscadden Bay, only metres from the restaurant and our fish is landed daily on Howth Pier. East Café Bar is open all day, with seating on the terrace.

Walking, golfing, sailing, paddle boarding, diving….Lots to do. Stay a few days!

Awards:

Food & Wine – Hall of Fame: Aidan & Joan Mac Manus.

National Hospitality Awards – overall winner Best Seafood Restaurant 2014.

Hot Press Best of Dublin 2016.

Bedrooms **8**   Guesthouse ★ ★ ★ ★

King Sitric, Fish Restaurant & Accommodation, East Pier, Howth, Co.Dublin D13 F5C6
T +353 (0)1 832 5235
info@kingsitric.ie
www.kingsitric.ie

Proprietors: The MacManus Family
Bed & Breakfast from €65 pps.
Special short breaks available.
Babies and children welcome – under 12s sharing with parents free.
Small dogs by arrangement.
Dinner Wednesday – Saturday from 6.30pm.
Sundays 1.00pm – 5.00pm.
East Café Bar open every day from 10.30am.
Private Dining, Weddings, Meetings, etc.
Closed last 2 weeks Jan.

How to find:
Coming in to Howth, all the way across the harbour front to the end of the road, top of the far pier.

GPS coordinates
Latitude 53.23 18 N
Longitude 06.03 48 W

L'ECRIVAIN

Michelin Starred l'Ecrivain Restaurant, in the heart of Georgian Dublin, since 1989. This modern contemporary multi Award winning restaurant is run by Chef Derry Clarke, his wife Sallyanne with a dedicated professional Front of House & Kitchen Team. We have a reputation for innovative cooking Irish/French Style, using only the finest freshest ingredients from artisan producers, always in season, in a convivial atmosphere with luxurious surroundings.

As well as our beautifully appointed dining room, l'Ecrivain has three Private Rooms: The Malt Room, seats 12 comfortably; Our Chef's Samsung Kitchen, a new addition, is a Private Room with a 'live' kitchen where our team of chefs cook for and in front of our guests. The Salon Privee seats up to 20 people max, with separate access to our roof terrace – a must when the sun shines.

We cater for Corporate Events, Weddings and Private Parties.

Awards:
Best Chef Ireland 2015 & 2016 **Good Eating Guide.**
Best Chef Dublin 2015 **Food & Wine Magazine.**

---

l'Ecrivain Restaurant
109a Lower Baggot Street, Dublin 2
T +353 (0)1 661 1919
F +353 (0)1 661 0617
enquiries@lecrivain.com
www.lecrivain.com

Proprietors: Derry and Sallyanne Clarke
Extensive Wine List and Cocktail List available.
Main Restaurant seats 90.
The Malt Room – Private Dining Room seats 12.
Salon Privè – Private Dining Room seats 18.
Chef's Samsung Kitchen seats 20.
Lunch: Thursday and Friday 12.30pm to 2.00pm.
Dinner: Monday to Saturday 6.30pm to 10.30pm.
Reservations recommended.

The 163 acres Estate offers accommodation in a style which blends contemporary design with old world charm, from the 19th Century Georgian Country House with adjacent Garden Mews to the Victorian Lake Lodge overlooking the beautiful Lake Abisdealy.

A magically timeless place, Liss Ard offers an ideal escape for those seeking a little time out. From the natural environment of its extensive gardens, containing the unique James Turrell "Irish Sky Garden", to the quiet solitude of its private lake, Liss Ard will remain in your thoughts long after you have returned home. Perfect for a weekend getaway or planning the wedding of your dreams.

Our culinary team offers you exquisite food in a modern Irish style, presenting fresh, clean flavors complementing the many local food artisans of West Cork.

Awards include: **One Fab Day** Top 51 Exclusive Wedding Venues in Ireland. **Trip Advisor Certificate** of excellence 2014, 2015, 2016. **Michelin Guide** 2016.

Bedrooms/Suites **25**   **Luxury Country House & Estate**

Liss Ard Estate, Castletownshend Road, Skibbereen, Co.Cork
T:+353 (0)28 40000
F:+353 (0)28 40001
reservations@lissard.com
www.lissardestate.com

Rooms from €50pps – €150pps.
À la carte Dinner, 3 course from €35pp.
Open all year for weddings, groups and special events.

How to find:
Liss Ard is two minutes from Skibbereen town centre. From Cork Airport, follow the N71 to West Cork & Skibbereen. At Skibbereen follow the one way system to the Regal Roundabout with the VW dealership. Take the first exit and follow the signs to Castletownshend, A596. The entrance to the Liss Ard Estate is less than 1 kilometre on the right-hand-side.

GPS coordinates
51.532348250305326
(Latitude)
-9.249801635742188
(Longitude)

LONGUEVILLE HOUSE

Nestled in 500 acres of wooded estate, Longueville House (c1720) is a romantic Georgian Heritage Mansion owned and run by the O'Callaghan family. An ideal location for romantic breaks, private house parties, celebrations, meetings & exclusive residential wedding parties. Longueville offers on-site salmon & brown trout fishing on the River Blackwater, Simulated Clay Shooting, May Dawn Chorus Walks & Autumn Mushroom Hunts. A Walled Kitchen Garden & Working Farm, Brandy Distillery & Cider House all to explore on-site! At the heart of Longueville is The Presidents' Restaurant, with a field to fork policy offering the freshest produce from our gardens & farm with kitchen supervised by internationally commended chef/patron William O'Callaghan.

Recent Awards Include:
One Fab Day 100 Best Wedding Venues 2015, 2014, 2013.
Irish Food Awards 2014, 2013 for Apple Brandy – Spirits Section.
Trip Advisor Travellers Choice 2015.

Bedrooms **14**   Junior Suites **6**   Listed Heritage Property ★ ★ ★ ★

**Longueville House and Presidents'
Restaurant, Mallow, Co.Cork**
T +353 (0)22 47156
F +353 (0)22 47459
info@longuevillehouse.ie
www.longuevillehouse.ie

Proprietor: The O'Callaghan Family
Rates: Bed & Breakfast €95 – €150 pps. Single supplements apply. Dinner menu from €65, served 6.30 – 8.30pm. Open Wednesday to Sunday inclusive year round. Opens for groups 20 Guests + Mon/Tues by prior arrangement. Winter opening hours more limited, consult hotel website.

How to find:
3 miles west of Mallow via the N72 road to Killarney. Take the second Ballyclough junction on the right hand side (approx. 3 miles from Mallow roundabout) and hotel entrance is 100 yards on left-hand side where a warm welcome awaits.

GPS coordinates
N52° 08. 308
W008° 44.188

MARLFIELD HOUSE

Marlfield is a beautifully restored charming Regency period house set on 36 acres of gardens and filled with gleaming antiques and paintings. It is situated outside the prosperous town of Gorey, well known for its boutiques and just 45 minutes south of Dublin. It's elegant and luxurious bedrooms overlook the extensive grounds and gardens.

The fine dining restaurant, housed in the Turner conservatory with frescoed walls, is highly acclaimed and open from Wednesday to Sunday. Alternatively 'The Duck' terrace restaurant, café and bar was opened in converted courtyard buildings in June 2015 and provides a popular and casual alternative serving European food for lunch and dinner daily.

Marlfield hosts exclusive use house wedding parties. Delicious food, luxurious surroundings and impeccable service provide the romantic and ultimate escape from it all.

Restaurant Association of Ireland: Best Customer Service Award in Leinster 2013, 2014, 2015.
One Fab Day 100 Best Wedding Venues 2013 to 2016.

Bedrooms **13**   State Rooms **6**

Marlfield House, Courtown Road R742, Gorey, Co.Wexford
T +353 (0)53 94 21124
info@marlfieldhouse.ie
www.marlfieldhouse.com

Proprietor: The Bowe Family
General Managers: Margaret and Laura Bowe
Open 2nd February to 2nd January.
Open all year for weddings and special events.
B&B: Bedrooms from €90 – €128 pps.
State Bedrooms: €190 – €310 pps.
Supper Menu from €36, Sunday lunch €45,
Five course dinner €65.
The Duck open daily from 11.30 for coffees,
cocktails, lunch and dinner.

How to find:
Marlfield is 75km south of Dublin off the N11 and is located just outside the town of Gorey on the Courtown Road R742. From Exit 23 on the N11 follow signs for Courtown, at Courtown Road roundabout turn left for Gorey. Follow signs for Marlfield.

GPS coordinates
N 52 40 06
W 06 16 46

THE MERRION HOTEL

The Merrion, Dublin's most stylish 5 star hotel is situated opposite Government Buildings in the city centre. Created from four Georgian Townhouses and a contemporary Garden Wing, the 142 bedrooms and suites are arranged around beautifully manicured gardens. Stunningly restored interiors provide the backdrop for one of Ireland's most impressive art collections.

Guests have the choice of two bars and two restaurants, including the 2 Michelin - starred Restaurant Patrick Guilbaud.

Additional features include Georgian Drawing Rooms where Art Afternoon Tea is served daily, and The Tethra Spa which boasts an 18m pool, gymnasium, steam room and treatment rooms.

Recent Awards: 'Remarkably Uncommon Award' for The Art Experience at The Merrion – **Leading Hotels of the World** – 2015.
Readers Choice Awards – The Merrion was voted #1 hotel in Dublin – **Conde Nast Traveler** – 2015.
World's Best Hotels – **Travel & Leisure** – 2015.
Top 100 Hotels in the World – **Robb Report** – 2015.

Bedrooms **123**   Suites **19**   Hotel ★ ★ ★ ★ ★

The Merrion Hotel,
Upper Merrion Street, Dublin 2
T +353 (0)1 603 0600
F +353 (0)1 603 0700
info@merrionhotel.com
www.merrionhotel.com

General Manager: Peter MacCann
Published Rates:
From €505 – €3,410 per room, per night.

GDS Code: LW8430.

How to find:
Located in Dublin city centre on Upper Merrion Street, opposite Government Buildings.

GPS coordinates
Lat: 53.338596
Long: -6.252956

MOUNT JULIET
HOTEL & ESTATE

Steeped in heritage, Mount Juliet is one of Ireland's lavish country estates, famed for the welcome and exceptional service.

Experience everything Mount Juliet has to offer including dinner in the 1 Michelin Star Lady Helen restaurant, golf on the acclaimed Jack Nicklaus course recently voted best parkland course in Ireland, river & lake fishing, equestrian centre with extensive trails, woodland walks and much more.

Mount Juliet is a wonderfully relaxed location for a luxury break in the South East; located 20 minutes from the medieval city of Kilkenny & just over 1 hour from Dublin.

Recent Awards:
Hotel – Listed in Top 15 Hotels and Resorts in Ireland, as chosen by **Condé Nast Traveler.**
The Lady Helen Restaurant – 1 **Michelin** Star & 3 **AA** Rosettes.

Bedrooms **32**

Luxury Country House & Estate ★ ★ ★ ★

Mount Juliet Country Estate, Thomastown, Co.Kilkenny
T +353 (0)56 777 3000
info@mountjuliet.ie
www.mountjuliet.ie

General Manager: Christine Murphy
Open all year round.
Manor Superior King, from €205 – €355.

How to find:
From Dublin: Take the N7/M7 (Naas Road) – branch onto the M9, signposted 'Waterford, Carlow & Kilkenny' which is Exit 11 on the M7. Follow the M9 and take Exit 9 signposted 'Kilkenny/Stoneyford'. At the top of the ramp turn left onto the N10 heading for Stoneyford. Drive straight through the village of Stoneyford and at the end of the village at the fork in the road (at the school) take the left hand turn, signposted 'Mount Juliet 4km'. After 4km, Mount Juliet will be on the left.

GPS Coordinates:
N 52° 31' 33.00"
W 07° 11' 13.00"

MOY HOUSE

Moy House is a beautifully restored early 19th century house ideally situated 10 minutes from the Cliffs of Moher on the "Wild Atlantic Way"

9 individually designed bedrooms make Moy House the perfect "home away from home" offering warm hospitality in contemporary, elegant surroundings.

A dedicated "farm to fork" approach to food ensures dining at Moy House is a truly memorable experience. 20 acres provide an 'outdoor larder' for the kitchen, rearing pigs, lamb, chickens and beef to serve alongside seasonal vegetables grown in the kitchen gardens.

Located minutes from world famous championships links golf courses, Moy House is a haven for the keen golfer. Intimate venue for small weddings.

Awards include:
2 **AA** Rosettes for Culinary Excellence.
Food & Wine Magazine: 'Style Award' 2012.
Georgina Campbell's: 'Hideaway of the Year' 2013.
Irish Restaurant Awards 2016: "Best Customer Service" Clare.

Bedrooms **9**   Suites **1**   Guesthouse ★ ★ ★ ★

Moy House, Lahinch, Co.Clare
T +353 (0)65 708 2800
moyhouse@eircom.net
www.moyhouse.com

Proprietor: Antoin O'Looney
Closed November – March.
Double rooms €145 – €320 per room B&B.
Signature suites €280 – €395 per room B&B.
Special packages also available.
Gourmet Tasting Menu €60.

How to find:
Moy House is located 1km outside Lahinch on N67 Miltown Malbay Road.

Shannon airport 48km.
Lahinch Golf Course 2km.
Doonbeg Golf Course 28km.

GPS coordinates
Lat: 52.951381
Long: -9.346285

THE MUSTARD SEED COUNTRY HOUSE & RESTAURANT

Nestled in the heart of the Golden Vale, overlooking the rustic village of Ballingarry. On the doorstep to Adare, the restaurant is legendary with superb food and warm hospitality.

Sitting on seven acres of manicured lawns, orchard and a working kitchen garden, this eclectic, heritage hideaway is the perfect venue for special occasions, family weddings and civil ceremonies. The house looks across at Knockfierna, the highest peak in the Mid West landscape, the perfect trek for even the amateur walker. Close to Lough Gur, one of Ireland's finest archaeological and historical gems.

"combines country house luxury with award-winning cuisine, perfect for city-slickers in need of recharging." Amie-Jo Locke, Tatler magazine.

'Outstanding Guest Experience' 2016 by **Georgina Campbell**.
Included in **Trip Advisor's** Hall of Fame.
Onefabday 100 Best Wedding Venues 2016.
'Best Customer Service' 2014 **Food & Wine Awards**.
'Best Hotel Restaurant' 2014 **National Hospitality Awards**.

Bedrooms **14**   Suites **3**   Hotel ★ ★ ★ ★

The Mustard Seed,
Ballingarry, Co.Limerick
T +353 (0)69 68508
mustard@indigo.ie
www.mustardseed.ie

General Manager: John Edward Joyce
B&B rates: €70 – €165 pps.
Single supplement: From €25.
Classic House menu: €60.
Early Evening Dinner: €47.
Pets by arrangement.
Children welcome.
Wheelchair friendly.

How to find:
From Limerick: From the top of Adare village, take the N21 Killarney road for half a mile. Turn left at the first road junction to the left and follow the signposts for Ballingarry village.
From Kerry: Travel along the N21. Look for signs for Rathkeale. In Rathkeale town, follow the R518 for four miles to Ballingarry village.

GPS coordinates
Lat: 52.474672
Long: 8.864692

NEWFORGE HOUSE

With beautiful views of gardens and green fields, our lovingly restored 18th century home, set in 40 acres, offers peace and tranquility. A warm welcome and elegant rooms, with family antiques and modern luxuries, await you.

With only six bedrooms Newforge offers an intimate home from home experience. For breakfast, and in our daily changing dinner menu, you will find homegrown fruits and vegetables, and eggs from the chickens in our orchard, together with carefully chosen local produce.

Located a short drive from the shores of Lough Neagh and 30 minutes from Belfast, Newforge is the perfect base for exploring Northern Ireland.

Recent awards include:
RAI: Best Chef & Best Hotel Restaurant Co. Armagh 2016.
McKennas' Guides: Top 100 Places to Stay in Ireland 2016 & Country House of the Year 2015.
Licenced & Catering News: Guesthouse of the Year 2015 & 2016.
One Fab Day 100 Best Wedding Venues.

Bedrooms **6**   Guesthouse ★ ★ ★ ★ ★

Newforge House, 58 Newforge Road, Magheralin, Co.Armagh, BT67 0QL
T +44 (0)28 926 11255
enquiries@newforgehouse.com
www.newforgehouse.com

Proprietor: John & Louise Mathers
Open: 31 January – 21 December.
B&B rates: £65 – £99 pps.
Single Supplement from £25.
Special mid-week, weekend and multiple-night breaks available.
3 Course Dinner £44, served at 8pm,
Tues. – Sat. Available with 24 hour's notice.
Light meal options available on Sunday and Monday evenings.

How to find:
From Belfast: M1 West, exit 9, Moira follow 5km. In Magheralin left at Byrne's pub: left after national speed limit sign.
From Newry: A1 north towards Belfast. Follow c. 30km, exit Dromore onto B2 (Lurgan Road). Continue 8km, take right onto Newforge Road B9. Continue 1km: 200m on right after bridge.

GPS coordinates
N 54.4619 W -6.2577

NEWPORT HOUSE

A Historic Georgian House in gardens and park adjoining the town and overlooking the Newport river and quay. For two hundred years it was the home of the O'Donnells, once the Earls of Tir Connell.

Famous as an angling centre Newport House offers preserved salmon and sea trout fishing on the Newport river (8 miles) and Lough Beltra.

The cuisine is based on fresh local produce and is complemented by an extensive cellar which includes many of the classical vintages. The house is furnished with many fine antiques and paintings which provide an elegant setting for a quiet and relaxing holiday.

RAI "Best Wine Experience in Connaught" 2015.

Bedrooms **10**   Hotel ★ ★ ★ ★

Newport House, Newport, Co.Mayo
T +353 (0)98 41222
info@newporthouse.ie
www.newporthouse.ie

How to find:
In the town of Newport.

Proprietor: Kieran Thompson
Open 24th March – mid October.
B&B: from €95.00 – €125.00 Low Season
from €110.00 – €140.00 High Season.
No Single Supplement.
No Service Charge.
5 Course Dinner €68.00 also à la carte
from 7.00 pm., to last orders 9.00 pm.

NO. 1 PERY SQUARE

Overlooking the handsome, tree-lined Peoples Park in Limerick's historic Georgian Quarter, No.1 Pery Square is a luxurious and intimate boutique town house. Situated just 5 min's walk from the city centre & train/bus station.

The house comprises of 20 bedrooms all individually named and styled. Delicious food & wine served at Sash and the Park room lounge. No.1 also houses an organic VOYA spa tucked away in the vaulted cellar and its very own kitchen garden, rooms full of personality and style throughout and a boutique wine shop.

Owner operated and open all year. Guests can enjoy the wonderful Peoples Park, Hunt Museum, King Johns Castle and Riverside walks.

Awards Include:
Conde Nast Hot List Hotel 2009, **Tatler** Best Facial & Boutique Spa Award, **NHA** Best New Hotel 2009, **Gold medal Awards** Best wine experience, **McKenna's Guide** to 100 Best since 2011, Best 100 wedding venues **One Fab Day**, Recommended by **Alistair Sawdays.**

Bedrooms **20**   Club Rooms **15**   Period rooms **4**   Townhouse Suite **1**

No. 1 Pery Square Hotel & Spa
Georgian Quarter, Limerick, Ireland
T +353 (0)61 402402
info@oneperysquare.com
www.oneperysquare.com

Proprietor: Patricia Roberts
Club rooms from €67.50 – €112.50pps.
Period rooms from €97.50 – €125pps.
Suite €112.50 – €175pps.
Special midweek and weekend packages available.
Sash Early Evening Table D'hôte €29.
Sunday Lunch €29, Full a la carte available.

How to find:
Shannon Airport – 27,5 km,
Cork Airport, Dublin Airport – 200km
2 mins walk to O'Connell Street, Bus and train Station. 5 mins walk to Shopping.

GPS coordinates
52° 39' 29.12" N
8° 37' 48.17" W

PARK HOTEL KENMARE COUNTRY HOUSE & RESTAURANT

Since 1897 many world travellers have enjoyed the pleasure of the Park Hotel Kenmare and its renowned restaurant. Set in a heavenly location overlooking Kenmare Bay the hotel is in the heart of Ireland's most scenic countryside. All accommodations are spacious with sitting area, antique furnishings and original art while Deluxe and Suites enjoy a full sea view or private veranda.

Home to the Deluxe Destination Spa SÁMAS guests can experience the virtues of a true spa. This special and quite unique place blends healing and therapeutic traditions from the East and West with the life inspiring scenery of Kerry to revive the body, mind and soul.

Awards include:
"Best Spa In Ireland" **Spafinder 2015.**
"Best Facial In Ireland" **Tatler Spa Awards 2015.**
Gold Medal Nominee **2016 Best 5* Ireland.**

Bedrooms **37**   Suites **9**   Hotel ★ ★ ★ ★ ★

Park Hotel Kenmare, Kenmare,   **How to find:**
Co.Kerry   'Top of Town'.
T +353 (0)64 664 1200
F +353 (0)64 664 1402
info@parkkenmare.com
www.parkkenmare.com

Managing Director: John Brennan
Open February 17th 2017 – November 27th 2017.
Open for the Christmas festive season.
Double/Twin €145pps – €405pps.
Dinner €70.
Two Night Packages from €345pps.
Wheelchair facilities.
Children welcome.

RATHMULLAN HOUSE

With its stunning location on the shores of Lough Swilly, the beautifully maintained rolling front lawn, leads you on to a 2 mile golden sandy beach. The interior of this country house is relaxed and welcoming, with large open fires burning throughout the year.

Bedrooms range from romantic doubles with garden views to large garret rooms for families. An indoor pool and holistic treatments add to the relaxation.

In the Cook & Gardener restaurant, you will find fresh locally sourced produce including Donegal landed seafood. The Tap Room provides an informal dining option and is the home of locally brewed Kinnegar Beer.

Awards include:
One Fab Day – Top 100 Wedding Venues 2016.
John & Sally McKennas Guide – Top 100 Places to Stay & Eat 2016.

Bedrooms **32**   Hotel ★ ★ ★ ★

Rathmullan House, Rathmullan, Co.Donegal

T +353 (0)74 915 8188, F +353 (0)74 915 8200
info@rathmullanhouse.com
www.rathmullanhouse.com

Proprietor: The Wheeler Family
Open full time from: March to October,
Winter Weekends, Half Terms & New Year.
B&B from €85 – €120 pps low season.
From €110 – €135 pps high season.
Single rooms available at no supplement.
Children welcome, busy with extended families
during holiday times.
A la carte dinner available 6pm – 8.30pm.
10% Service charge on extras only.

How to find:
From Letterkenny go to Ramelton (R245) and on to Rathmullan (R247). Turn left at butchers, through village heading north and gates are on the right.

GPS coordinates
N 55.0989383
W 7.53266

RATHSALLAGH HOUSE

Converted from Queen Anne stables in 1798, Rathsallagh is a large comfortable house situated in hundreds of acres of peaceful parkland with a walled garden and surrounded by the magnificent Rathsallagh Golf Club, a championship course measuring in excess of 7,000 yards. Also close to Glendalough, the Wicklow mountains, The National Stud (with its Japanese Gardens) and the Curragh, yet Dublin Airport is less than one hour's drive.

Rathsallagh is renowned for the consistency of its restaurant over the past 30 years, showcasing Irish Country House cooking at its best.

Available for private parties and exclusive rental for all events from family celebrations, weddings, incentives to conferences and meetings catering for up to 250 guests.

Awards Include:
Just Ask Restaurant of the Month February 2015.
Hot Press Top 100 Restaurants Ireland 2015.
National Breakfast awards three times.
Irish Country House of the Year – twice.

Bedrooms **35**

Rathsallagh House, Dunlavin, Co.Wicklow
T +353 (0)45 403112, F +353 (0)45 403343
info@rathsallagh.com
www.rathsallagh.com

Proprietor: The O'Flynn Family
Open all year round.
Bed & Breakfast from €95 pps. Free Wi fi.
Single Supplement from €75.
Dinner from €40.
Open for Sunday lunch.
Prior reservation essential.
Available for private fully serviced rentals.
Site inspections by appointment only.

How to find:
Signposted from Dunlavin.
Less than 50 mins Dublin airport.
M50 for Kildare / South – N7 South.
Exit jct. 11 for M9 south. Exit jct. 3 left signposted.

RESTAURANT FORTY ONE

Under the expert guidance of award-winning Chef Graham Neville, Restaurant FortyOne has flourished.

Graham and his team create delicate, elegant dishes, using the finest ingredients from their very own garden in Kenah Hill, Killiney.

Looking over the beauty of Stephen's Green, the dining room of Restaurant FortyOne is an intimate and serene setting in the heart of Dublin city.

The staff, meanwhile, are attentive and mindful. This is fine-dining without the stuffiness.

Recent awards:

2013 & 2014 **Food and Wine Magazine** Best Dublin Restaurant.
2013 & 2014 **Food and Wine Magazine** Best Dublin Chef.
2014 **Food and Wine Magazine** Chef of the Year.

Restaurant Forty One
41 St Stephen's Green, Dublin 2
T +353 (0)1 662 0000
info@restaurantfortyone.ie
www.restaurantfortyone.ie

Proprietor: Olivia Gaynor Long
Opening Hours: Tuesday – Saturday.
(Lunch: 12.30pm – 2.30pm).
(Dinner: 5.30pm – 10.30pm).
Annual Holidays: First two weeks in August and
after lunch on December 24th – December 31st
for dinner.

How to find:
St. Stephen's Green East, opposite the Green.

Established in 1981, Restaurant Patrick Guilbaud is Ireland's top restaurant, holder of two Michelin stars as well as virtually all the top national and international awards. It is situated in an 18th century Georgian Townhouse adjoining the Merrion Hotel. It houses an impressive collection of Irish Art.

This bright, elegant restaurant, run by Stephane Robin, serves modern classic cuisine using the best Irish produce in season. Chef Guillaume Lebrun's signature dishes include the Lobster Ravioli, Roast Challans Duck, Assiette Gourmande au Chocolat.

The wine list is very impressive in both its depth and its range – do take time to peruse it.

Covers **85**

Restaurant Patrick Guilbaud,
21 Upper Merrion Street, Dublin 2
T +353 (0)1 6764 192
F +353 (0)1 6610 052
info@restaurantpatrickguilbaud.ie
www.restaurantpatrickguilbaud.ie

Proprietor: Patrick Guilbaud
Chef: Guillaume Lebrun
Manager: Stephane Robin
Open: Tuesday to Saturday.
Closed 25th December – 5th January.
Lunch: 12:30 – 2:15pm. Dinner: 7pm – 10:15pm.
Lunch Menu: €50 (2 Courses) €60 (3 Courses),
except December.
Special Christmas Lunch Menu €80 for
all December.

Seasonal Tasting Menu: €120,
available only from Tuesday to Friday.
A la Carte available Lunch & Dinner.
Private Dining Room.

How to find:
Opposite Government buildings.
Merrion Street.

ROSLEAGUE MANOR

A beautifully situated Georgian house overlooking Ballinakill Bay, which has been lovingly converted into a first-class hotel with a Victorian style conservatory and delightful drawing rooms with open log fires. All of the bedrooms are individually decorated and feature fine antiques and paintings.

Set in 30 acres of secluded woodland on the ocean's edge, Rosleague is located just one mile from the Connemara National Park, an area of some 5,000 acres and just 5 minutes drive from Kylemore Abbey and it's beautiful walled gardens.

Cuisine is based on the freshest and finest of ingredients, with local seafood and Connemara lamb a speciality.

Sunday Independent – *"As such, Rosleague Manor's Summer Eden is a hard stage to beat."*

One Fab Day – *"A Dazzling Dozen, 12 fabulous new Irish Wedding Venues."*

Tripadvisor – *'Top 10 Best Small Hotels in Ireland.'*

Bedrooms **16**   Junior Suites **4**   Listed Heritage Hotel ★ ★ ★ ★

Rosleague Manor, Letterfrack, Connemara, Co.Galway
T +353 (0)95 41101
F +353 (0)95 41168
info@rosleague.com
www.rosleague.com

Proprietors: Edmund and Mark Foyle
Open: 15 March – 1 November.
B&B from €80 – €125 pps.
Single supplement €36.
2 Course Dinner €36.
5 Course Dinner €50.
Special short break rates on request.
Dog Friendly.
Exclusive residential wedding parties: 100 max.

How to find:
N59, seven miles north west from Clifden.

GPS coordinates
N 53.5514
W 9.9716

A stunning 18th century Georgian house set in 80 acres of magnificent parkland, comprising superbly restored surrounding courtyards and walled gardens. Guests are offered the opportunity to experience genuine hospitality whilst enjoying the true feel of the quintessential Country House.

Situated at the heart of the Boyne Valley in the Heritage county of Meath. Tankardstown is 40 minutes from Dublin City and 30 minutes from Dublin Airport.

Stay in a main house heritage room or in a beautifully appointed court yard cottage. Enjoy simple food in our 'Cellar Restaurant' or more formal dining in our 2AA Rosette Brabazon Restaurant, located in the Tankardstown Garden Village.

Awards Include: **Georgina Campbell's** Country House of the Year 2015; **AA** Guest Accommodation of the Year 2013/2014; **Restaurants Association of Ireland'** Best Chef in Leinster 2015 & 2016; **Georgina Campbell's** Atmospheric Restaurant of the Year 2015.

Bedrooms **7** (main house)   **7** Chic Courtyard Cottages   Specialist Accommodation/
Failte Ireland's Welcome Standard

Tankardstown House, Nr. Slane, Rathkenny, Co.Meath
T +353 (0)41 982 4621
info@tankardstown.ie
www.tankardstown.ie

Proprietor: Brian & Trish Conroy
Open all year round.
Courtyard Room: €105 pps B&B.
Main House Heritage Bedroom: €335 per room B&B.
Master Suite: €360 per room B&B.

How to find:
From Dublin take the M1 motorway and exit at Junction 10. Follow the signs for Slane. Continue straight through the village on N51 — **or** — Take the N2 which will bring you directly into the village of Slane. Turn left at the traffic lights and continue through the village on N51. Come to main entrance gates to Slane Castle on your left. Directly opposite, turn right, at the fork STAY LEFT, and follow straight along this road for 4km. Signposted 'Tankardstown'.

GPS coordinates
N 53° 44' 27"
W 6° 36' 41"

Since Paul and Máire Flynn opened The Tannery in 1997, it has become one of the most original and welcoming experiences in Irish food. What makes it special? There is Paul's cooking, of course – his fresh Waterford ingredients, ever-changing menus and mouth-watering focus on local produce. There is our unique location in the seaside town of Dungarvan, a stone's throw from the Copper Coast and Comeragh Mountains. But most of all, there is the Tannery's knack for serving up that most important of ingredients: a great time.

Staying overnight in the Tannery Townhouse, our compact and cosy rooms in the heart of downtown Dungarvan completes the Tannery experience.

Awards Include:
McKenna Guides 100 Best Places to Eat and 100 Best Places to Stay 2016.
RAI Cookery School of the Year 2016.

Bedrooms **14**   Failte Ireland Welcome Standard 2017

Tannery Restaurant, Townhouse and Cookery School, Dungarvan, Co.Waterford
T +353 (0) 58 45420
info@tannery.ie
www.tannery.ie

Proprietor: Paul and Máire Flynn
Normal Opening Times:
Dinner Tuesday to Saturday.
Lunch Friday and Sunday.
Open weekday lunch July and August.
Open Sunday evenings bank holiday weekends and July, August.
Closed two weeks end January, beginning February.
Double rooms from €115 including breakfast.

How to find:
At end lower Main Street, beside Old Market House Building.
For Tannery Townhouse, please check in at Tannery Restaurant.

VIEWMOUNT HOUSE COUNTRY HOUSE & RESTAURANT

Discover this boutique gem, a secret tucked away in the heart of Ireland. This magnificent 17th century country house is complemented by its incredible countryside surroundings, and by the four acres of meticulously-maintained garden that surround it. Within the house you will find open fires, beautiful furniture, fresh flowers and Irish literature. It retains its stately, historic charm, and blends it with thoughtful renovation that incorporates modern comfort.

Enjoy Viewmount's exquisite dining experience - VM Restaurant is candlelit, with exposed stone walls, contemporary paintings, linen tablecloths. It is these aspects with the impeccable service, that create a superb atmosphere in which to relax.

Awards include:

Food & Wine: Best Chef Leinster – Gary O'Hanlon 2016.
Georgina Campbell Guide: Best Sunday Lunch 2012 & Best Restaurant 2014.
RAI Awards: Best Chef Leinster – Gary O'Hanlon 2013.
John & Sally Mc Kenna's Guide 100 Best to Eat & Stay.
One Fab Day Best 100 Wedding Venues.

Bedrooms **12**   Guesthouse ★ ★ ★ ★

Viewmount House
Dublin Road, Longford, N39 N2X6
T + 353 (0)43 3341919
info@viewmounthouse.com
www.viewmounthouse.com

Proprietor: Beryl & James Kearney
Closed 30 October – 8 November 2017.
Closed 24 – 27 December 2017.
Bed & Breakfast: €70.00 – €120.00pps.
Restaurant:
Open Wed. to Sat.: 6.30pm to 9.30pm.
Early Menu (Wed. – Fri.): €35.00 – €40.00.
5 Course Dinner: €60.00 – €70.00.
Lunch (Sunday only) 1.00pm to 4.00pm: €35.00.
All major credit cards accepted.

How to find:
From Dublin: Take M4 / N4 (Sligo). At the first roundabout entering Longford town, take first exit. Continue for .75km., sign for Viewmount House and VM Restaurant is on the left. Turn left at this junction. Continue for approx 800 m and entrance is on the right.
Longford town centre:
Take R393 (Ardagh), drive 1km and take the first slip road to the right, 800m, entrance is on the right.

GPS coordinates
53.72246
-7.77105

Nestled on Lough Ree in an idyllic rural setting, Wineport Lodge is just over an hour from Dublin, less from Galway.

Luxury rooms and suites and a reputation for excellent food, served in an unfussed way, make Wineport Lodge an ideal choice for a relaxing stay, lazy lunch or laid back afternoon tea.

Guest facilities include Treatment Suite and Hot Tub. Bikes rides, boat trips and woodland walks start right at the door. Glasson village with its traditional pubs, craft shop and gallery is a stroll away.

'This cedar-clad log cabin style lodge jutting out onto the lake shows the midlands at its most alluring,' Manchan Magan, Irish Times.

'Imagine a secluded wooden hotel built on the edge of a beautiful lake, with windows facing west; balconies on which to drink in the heavenly, endlessly changing views; wood-burning stoves; superb cuisine – and a delightfully relaxed vibe. That's Wineport!,' Neil Hegarty, The Telegraph.

Bedrooms / Suites **30**   Hotel ★ ★ ★ ★

**Wineport Lodge, Glasson,
Athlone, Co.Westmeath**
T +353 (0)90 643 9010
lodge@wineport.ie
www.wineport.ie

Proprietors: Ray Byrne and Jane English
Open all year round.
Closed 24 – 26 December.
Rooms from €75 pps B&B.
Suites from €90 pps B&B.
Afternoon tea from €25pp.
All Day Dining Menu.
A La Carte Dinner Menu.
Sunday Lunch (4 course): €39 pp.

How to find:
Take exit 10 off M6/N6 Dublin-Galway.
Follow N55 direction Cavan. At Ballykeeran fork
left at Dog & Duck pub. Then 1.6 kilometres
(1 mile) on left hand side.

GPS coordinates
N 53.465161
W -7.884579

COOLMORE MANOR HOUSE

A luxurious early 19th century Georgian Holiday Home with breath-taking ocean views overlooking Donegal Bay set on 11 acres of pasture land.

An elegant yet cosy "home away from home" on the Wild Atlantic Way in Co.Donegal, where a contemporary ambience is combined with antique furniture and warm hospitality.

Ideally located within walking distance to the sandy beach of Rossnowlagh. Several famous golf courses are within easy reach.

Available on site are Massages, Physiotherapy, Seaweed Baths, a Hot Tub with ocean views and a Sauna. As well as a walled flower garden, Bellavista viewpoint, a small Showjumping Horse Stud and on request Lobster Dinner.

Bedrooms **3 double ensuite,** additional separate **Apartment for 1-2** available

Failte Ireland ★ ★ ★ ★ ★

Coolmore Manor House
Rossnowlagh, Co.Donegal
T +353 (0)71 985 9997
info@coolmoremanorhouse.com
www.coolmoremanorhouse.com

Proprietors: The Schwander Family
Self Catering.
Weekly Rentals. Shorter stays available in low season or on short notice.
Open all year round.
Not suitable for children under 16.
Low Season: €1,985 – €2,835.
High Season: €2,205 – €3,150.
Christmas/New Year: €3,570.
Rates include: Heating, Electricity, Water, Wi-Fi, VAT, Bedlinens, Towels, Secure Private Parking, Final Cleaning and a Welcome Aperitif.

How to find:
7km outside of Ballyshannon on the Rossnowlagh coastal Road R231. We can send you a map with directions prior to your journey.
From Dublin Airport: ~ 3 hours
From Belfast Airport: ~ 2,5 hours
From Knock Airport: ~ 1,5 hours
From Shannon Airport: ~ 4 hours.

GPS coordinates
N 54.543194
W 08.218031

SHANNON PRINCESS

The Shannon Princess is a luxury boutique hotel barge cruising the river Shannon in Ireland. Family run and with a professional crew, the Shannon Princess is the perfect way to explore what the river and her loughs have to offer. Guests on board will enjoy all the indulgent comforts of their own private floating luxury hotel, an unforgettable experience that will create memories forever.

Cruises are of a 6 night / 7 day duration, which can be booked by the cabin or as an exclusive Charter for up to 10 guests. Itineraries choices include Classic, Walking, Golf and Family Cruises. On board contemporary luxury seamlessly blends with a welcoming atmosphere and casual informality. Deluxe accommodations include Air Conditioning, a deck side Spa pool and delicious cuisine and wines.

Acolades: Shannon Princess is featured in **Chris Santella's book**, **Once in a Lifetime Trips** "The World's 50 most Extraordinary and Memorable Travel Experiences."
Distinctive Destinations for Discerning Travellers: *"If the Shannon Princess were land locked, it would be a Michelin Star Restaurant."*

Bedrooms **5 ensuite cabins**

Shannon Princess, Glasson, Athlone, Co.Westmeath
T +353 (0)87 2514809
info@shannonprincess.com
www.shannonprincess.com

Proprietor: The Gibbons Family
Low season: April 23 – May 13. US$4,400 per person. Charter for 10 is US$41,500. Charter for 8 is US$39,300. Charter for 6 is US$37,100.
High season: May 14 – Oct 1. US$5,050 per person. Charter for 10 is US$47,000. Charter for 8 is US$44,200. Charter for 6 is US$41,400.

How to find:
Departures are from Glasson, Athlone to Killaloe and every second week from Killaloe to Glasson.

TRAVEL NOTES

_____

_____

_____

_____

_____

_____

_____

_____

_____

_____

_____

_____

_____

_____

_____

_____

_____

_____

There are no strangers here,
only friends that have not yet met.

WILLIAM BUTLER YEATS

COME DINE WITH US

IRELAND'S BLUE BOOK

Make Business a Pleasure

Searching for an inspirational location for your next conference, corporate meeting, exhibition, gala dinner or a one-off social event or incentive? Look no further than Ireland's Blue Book.

Located throughout the island of Ireland these properties will make the perfect location for your business event.

Blue Book Gift Vouchers are an ideal Corporate Gift.

www.irelands-blue-book.ie/meetings.html / T +353 1 676 9914

Historic Hotels of Europe

www.historichotelsofeurope.com

Austria
Schlosshotels & Herrenhäuser
info@schlosshotels.co.at
www.schlosshotels.co.at

Norway
De Historiske
info@dehistoriske.no
www.dehistoriske.com

Belgium & Netherlands
Hampshire Hotels
info@hampshire-hotels.com
www.hampshire-hotels.com/historic

Portugal
Hotels Heritage Lisboa
heritage.hotels@heritage.pt
www.heritage.pt

France
Symboles de France
contact@symbolesdefrance.com
www.symbolesdefrance.com

Slovakia
Historic Hotels of Slovakia
info@historichotelsofslovakia.com
www.historichotelsofslovakia.com

Greece
Yades Greek Historic Hotels
welcome@yadeshotels.gr
www.yadeshotels.gr

Sweden
Countryside Hotels
info@countrysidehotels.se
www.countrysidehotels.se

Hungary
Hungarian Castle Hotels Association
www.hungariancastlehotels.com
info@hungariancastlehotels.com

Switzerland
Swiss Historic Hotels
info@swiss-historic-hotels.com
www.swiss-historic-hotels.com

Ireland
Ireland's Blue Book
mail@irelandsbluebook.com
www.irelandsbluebook.com

Wales
Welsh Rarebits
info@rarebits.co.uk
www.rarebits.co.uk

Italy
Abitare La Storia
mailbox@abitarelastoria.it
www.abitarelastoria.it

Historic Hotels of Europe
is affiliated with

HISTORIC HOTELS
of **AMERICA**
NATIONAL TRUST **FOR HISTORIC PRESERVATION**

WHERE MOMENTS
ARE TREASURED

More than 80 boutiques with savings of up to 60%*,
including Só Collective – a new home for Irish fashion,
design and craft, exclusive to Kildare Village.

KILDARE VILLAGE

HOUSE OF
WATERFORD
CRYSTAL

See Exquisite Pieces of Crystal
manufactured before your eyes

Waterford
Crystal Factory
and Brand
Experience

The House of Waterford Crystal brings a visit to Waterford to a whole new level, as visitors can witness the creation of crystal masterpieces right before their very eyes. The factory tour is a unique and captivating experience that allows people go behind the scenes for over an hour and see exactly how Waterford Crystal pieces are made and they can witness every stage of production, from the initial design stage right up to the final engraving of the piece.

Guided Factory Tours Daily
Waterford Brand & Visitor Experience

Open Daily

Book online at **www.waterfordvisitorcentre.com** and receive a 10% discount on adult tickets

Phone +353 (0) 51 317000

www.waterfordvisitorcentre.com

YOUR SOMETHING BLUE…
IRELAND'S MOST ROMANTIC WEDDING VENUES

Each house or restaurant has a reference number which relates to both the map opposite and the page on which it appears.

1. **Aherne's Townhouse**
   Tel: +353 (0)24 92424
   E-mail: info@ahernes.net

2. **Ardtara Country House & Restaurant**
   Tel: +44 (0)28 796 44490
   From Republic: 048 796 44490
   E-mail: info@ardtara.com

3. **Ballymaloe House**
   Tel: +353 (0)21 465 2531
   E-mail: res@ballymaloe.ie

4. **Barberstown Castle**
   Tel: +353 (0)1 628 8157
   E-mail: info@barberstowncastle.ie

5. **Belleek Castle**
   Tel: +353 (0) 96 22 400
   E-mail: info@belleekcastle.com

6. **Blairscove Restaurant and Accommodation**
   Tel: +353 (0)27 61127
   E-mail: mail@blairscove.ie

7. **Browns Restaurant & Champagne Lounge**
   Tel: +44 (0)28 7134 5180
   E-mail: eat@brownsrestaurant.com

8. **Bushmills Inn**
   Tel: +44 (0)28 207 33000
   From Republic: 048 207 33000
   E-mail: mail@bushmillsinn.com

9. **Campagne Restaurant**
   Tel: +353 (0)56 777 2858
   E-mail: info@campagne.ie

10. **Carrig Country House & Restaurant**
    Tel: +353 (0)66 976 9100
    E-mail: info@carrighouse.com

11. **Cashel House Hotel**
    Tel: +353 (0)95 31001
    E-mail: sales@cashelhouse.ie

12. **Castle Durrow**
    Tel: +353 (0)57 873 6555
    E-mail: info@castledurrow.com

13. **Castle Leslie Estate**
    Tel: +353 (0)47 88100
    E-mail: info@castleleslie.com

14. **Chapter One Restaurant**
    Tel: +353 (0)1 873 2266
    E-mail: info@chapteronerestaurant.com

15. **Clare Island Lighthouse**
    Tel: +353 (0)87 668 9758
    E-mail: info@clareislandlighthouse.com

16. **Coopershill House**
    Tel: +353 (0)71 916 5108
    E-mail: ohara@coopershill.com

17. **Currarevagh House**
    Tel: +353 (0)91 552312 / 552313
    E-mail: rooms@currarevagh.com

18. **Dunbrody House**
    Tel: +353 (0)51 389600
    E-mail: info@dunbrodyhouse.com

19. **Enniscoe House**
    Tel: +353 (0)96 31112
    E-mail: mail@enniscoe.com

20. **Ghan House**
    Tel: +353 (0)42 937 3682
    E-mail: info@ghanhouse.com

21. **Gregans Castle Hotel**
    Tel: +353 (0)65 707 7005
    E-mail: stay@gregans.ie

22. **Hayfield Manor**
    Tel: +353 (0)21 484 5900
    E-mail: enquiries@hayfieldmanor.ie

23. **Hilton Park**
    Tel: +353 (0)47 56007
    E-mail: mail@hiltonpark.ie

24. **Hunter's Hotel**
    Tel: +353 (0)404 40106
    E-mail: reception@hunters.ie

25. **Ice House**
    Tel: +353 (0)96 23500
    E-mail: chill@theicehouse.ie

26. **Killarney Royal**
    Tel: +353 (0)64 6631853
    E-mail: reception@killarneyroyal.ie

27. **King Sitric Fish Restaurant & Accommodation**
    Tel: +353 (0)1 832 5235
    E-mail: info@kingsitric.ie

28. **L'Ecrivain Restaurant**
    Tel: +353 (0)1 661 1919
    E-mail: enquiries@lecrivain.com

29. **Liss Ard Estate**
    Tel: +353 (0)28 40000
    E-mail: reservations@lissardestate.com

30. **Longueville House**
    Tel: +353 (0)22 47156
    E-mail: info@longuevillehouse.ie

31. **Marlfield House**
    Tel: +353 (0)53 94 21124
    E-mail: info@marlfieldhouse.ie

32. **Merrion Hotel**
    Tel: +353 (0)1 603 0600
    E-mail: info@merrionhotel.com

33. **Mount Juliet Hotel & Estate**
    Tel: +353 (0)56 777 3000
    E-mail: info@mountjuliet.ie

34. **Moy House**
    Tel: +353 (0)65 708 2800
    E-mail: moyhouse@eircom.net

35. **The Mustard Seed**
    Tel: +353 (0)69 68508
    E-mail: mustard@indigo.ie

36. **Newforge House**
    Tel: +44 (0)28 926 11255
    From Republic: 048 926 11255
    E-mail: enquiries@newforgehouse.com

37. **Newport House**
    Tel: +353 (0)98 41222
    E-mail: info@newporthouse.ie

38. **No. 1 Pery Square**
    Tel: +353 (0)61 402402
    E-mail: info@oneperysquare.com

39. **Park Hotel Kenmare**
    Tel: +353 (0)64 664 1200
    E-mail: info@parkkenmare.com

40. **Rathmullan House**
    Tel: +353 (0)74 915 8188
    E-mail: info@rathmullanhouse.com

41. **Rathsallagh House**
    Tel: +353 (0)45 403112
    E-mail: info@rathsallagh.com

42. **Restaurant Forty One**
    Tel: +353 (0)1 662 0000
    E-mail: info@restaurantfortyone.com

43. **Restaurant Patrick Guilbaud**
    Tel: +353 (0)1 6764 192
    E-mail: info@restaurantpatrickguilbaud.ie

44. **Rosleague Manor**
    Tel: +353 (0)95 41101
    E-mail: info@rosleague.com

45. **Tankardstown House**
    Tel: +353 (0)41 982 4621
    E-mail: info@tankardstown.ie

46. **The Tannery**
    Tel: +353 (0) 58 45420
    E-mail: info@tannery.ie

47. **Viewmount House**
    Tel: + 353 (0)43 3341919
    E-mail: info@viewmounthouse.com

48. **Wineport Lodge**
    Tel: +353 (0)90 643 9010
    E-mail: lodge@wineport.ie

49. **Coolmore Manor House**
    Tel: +353 (0)71 985 9997
    E-mail: info@coolmoremanorhouse.com

50. **Shannon Princess**
    Tel: +353 (0)87 2514809
    E-mail: info@shannonprincess.com

PRIVATE RENTAL